An amusing, enlightening history of how and why standard units of measurement of length came into being.

"An inch," decreed Edward II in the 14th century, "is the length of 3 barley corns, round and dry, taken from the center of the ear, and laid end to end."

The first recorded unit of length came thousands of years before this in Egypt and Babylonia. This was the cubit, the distance from elbow to tip of the middle finger.

Units of measurement have come in answer to the needs of commerce, industry and science.

Three barley corns cannot serve the engineers who must be exact to the millionth of a standard inch.

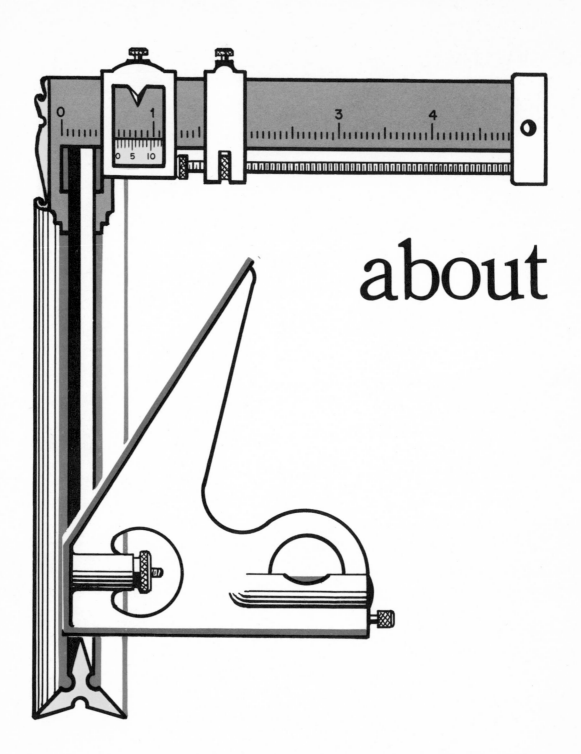

about

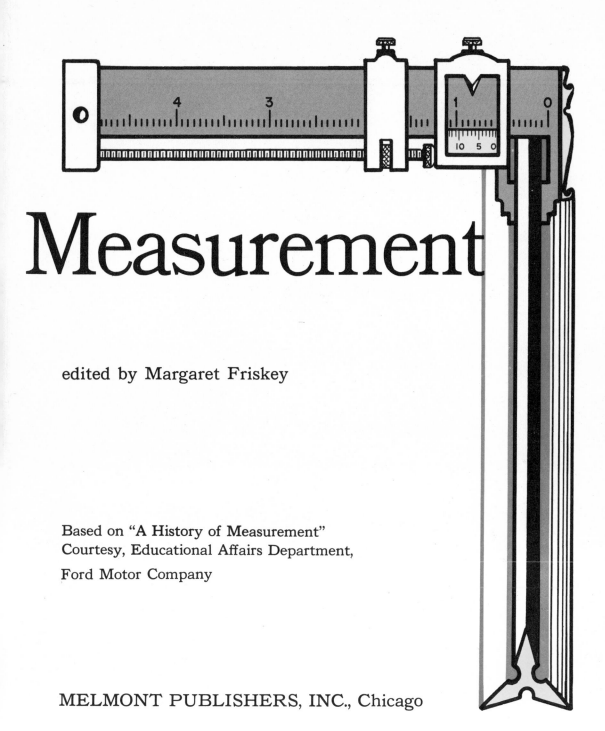

Measurement

edited by Margaret Friskey

Based on "A History of Measurement"
Courtesy, Educational Affairs Department,

Ford Motor Company

MELMONT PUBLISHERS, INC., Chicago

Library of Congress Catalog Card Number: 65-24614

This edition published through the courtesy of the
Educational Affairs Department, Ford Motor Company.

Copyright © 1965 Melmont Publishers, Inc.
Printed in the U.S.A.
Published simultaneously in Canada

2 3 4 5 6 7 8 9 10 11 12 13 14 15 16 17 18 19 20 21 22 23 24 25   R   75 74 73 72 71 70 69 68 67 66

THE BEGINNING

How long was the fish?

So long. A caveman used arms, fingers, or hands to show length.

Primitive man may have had some ideas about long and short, or far and near.

This was all he needed for the way he lived. There were no inches, feet, yards, fathoms, meters, or other units of measurement in his life. He had no need of them.

The story of how and why units of measurement of length came into being is interesting and amusing.

THE CUBIT

The cubit, used in Egypt and Babylonia, was the first unit of measurement recorded in history. A cubit was the length of the forearm from elbow to tip of the middle finger. Its symbol was a picture of a forearm.

The people in Egypt and Babylonia needed a unit of measurement. They were building cities, great pyramids, and temples.

These early builders used stones. How big should they be? Workmen could be told to use stones that were two cubits long. They could understand length that was expressed in units of measurement. However, a cubit was not always the same. Some forearms were longer than others.

THE CUBIT

THE FOOT

Many, many years later, the Greeks and the Romans were using the cubit.

They called it the Olympic cubit. Unlike the Egyptian cubit, the Olympic cubit was always the same length. It was equal to 18.24 inches.

Two-thirds of the Olympic cubit became the first unit of measurement called a foot.

As the Roman soldiers marched across the world, they brought the foot measurement to the nations they conquered, including Great Britain.

THE FOOT

THE INCH

The Greeks went a step further. They divided the foot into twelve thumbnail widths. The Romans called these "unicae," meaning "twelfths."

The Anglo-Saxons in England changed "unicae" to "inch."

In the 14th century, King Edward II decreed:

> "One inch is the length of three barley corns, round and dry, taken from the center of the ear and laid end to end."

THE INCH

THE FATHOM

The English were sailors. It was often important to them to know just how deep the water was. They developed a unit of measurement for depth.

A sailor put a weight on the end of a line and dropped it overboard. Then he measured the wet line with outstretched arms.

The word "fathom" meant "out-stretched arms." He could call out, "Two fathoms!" and everyone aboard would know that the water was about twelve feet deep.

Depth of water is still expressed in fathoms. However, now, a fathom is always six feet.

THE FATHOM

THE YARD

The English were beginning to make and sell cloth. The merchants who sold it had to think up a way to measure it.

At first they sold it by the half a fathom. This was the distance from the middle of the chest to the finger tip of an outstretched arm. The word they used for this length was "yard."

The merchant with short arms could sell shorter yards than one with long arms.

THE YARD

THE STANDARD YARD

King Henry I decreed that a lawful yard was the distance from the point of HIS nose to the end of the thumb on HIS outstretched arm.

The lawmakers made a note of this.

This was a step toward making the yard a standard length.

Then along came King Henry VII who ruled that a yard be exactly three feet.

He had this measure marked on a bronze yard bar.

THE STANDARD YARD

THE ROD

At one time an acre of land was the amount of land that a pair of oxen could plow in one day. But what a difference hard, rocky ground could make, or old, slow oxen.

The English kings wanted a more exact way of measuring an acre.

It was decreed that an acre was a piece of land 40 poles long and 4 poles wide. The length of the pole was determined by lining up sixteen men as they left church on Sunday morning.

We now say "rod" instead of "pole." Its length is 16½ feet, or 5½ yards.

THE ROD

THE FURLONG

A fathom was a unit of measurement that sailors used.

The yard was related to trade goods.

The rod, longer than both the yard and the fathom, was used in measuring land.

English farmers also used the furlong as a measurement of length. A furlong at first was "one furrow long" in a plowed field.

Today the furlong is 40 rods, or one-eighth of a mile.

Races are sometimes run in furlongs.

THE FURLONG

THE METER

During the French Revolution, French scientists proposed a whole new system of measurement. They did not set it up by decree, nor did they reckon it in arm lengths.

These scientists found one ten-millionth of the distance from the equator to either pole. They called it a meter. Then they set up the metric system of reckoning by tens and tenths.

The standard meter is shown as the distance between two lines on a platinum-iridium bar at the International Bureau of Weights and Measures in Paris. This bar is kept under constant temperature.

A meter is a little longer than a yard. It is about 39.37 inches.

A kilometer is a thousand meters, about five-eighths of a mile.

A centimeter is one-hundredth of a meter.

22

THE METER

THE DECIMAL INCH

In the United States, both English and metric measurements are used. Sometimes they are combined, as in the decimal-inch system.

An automobile motor may have as many as 13,000 parts that must fit together. Many of these parts must be accurate beyond a thousandth of an inch (a mil).

Accurate systems of measurement have become necessary for every product manufactured and for every field of science.

THE DECIMAL INCH

SCIENTIFIC TERMS

Scientists work with measurements too small to be seen. And they work with measurements almost too big to be imagined.

The angstrom, named after a Swedish physicist, measures only 264-millionths of an inch.

On the other hand, a light-year is defined as the distance a beam of light travels in one year. Since light travels at 186,281 miles per second, a light-year is about six trillion miles!

Distances to stars are measured in light-years.

Alpha Centauri, the nearest star beyond the sun, is more than four light-years **away.**

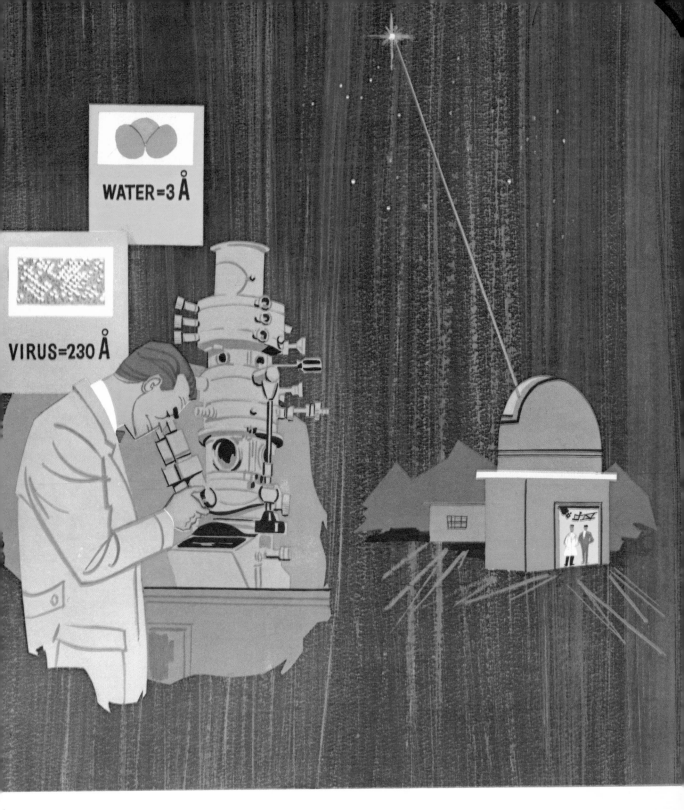

WATER = 3 Å

VIRUS = 230 Å

SCIENTIFIC TERMS

THE SPACE AGE

This book has tried to show how the need for measuring length led to the development of units of measurement.

Now, in this space age, scientists measure many things besides length. They have made instruments that measure radiation from the moon and planets. They measure force and time and size and weight. They measure arcs and angles. Everything!

Measure by measure, they reach for the stars.

THE SPACE AGE

SYSTEMS
OF MEASUREMENT

American & British Linear System

12 inches. . . . . .1 foot
3 feet. . . . . .1 yard
2 yards. . . . . .1 fathom
5½ yards. . . . . .1 rod
220 yards. . . . . .1 furlong
1,760 yards. . . . . . . .1 mile

The metric system of measurement is universally used in areas of science. The British may convert to the metric system for more general use.

A meter (about 39.37 inches) is a little longer than a yard. A kilometer (a thousand meters) is about five-eighths of a mile. A centimeter is one-hundredth of a meter.

European Metric System

10 millimeters....1 centimeter
10 centimeters...1 decimeter
10 decimeters....1 meter
10 meters........1 dekameter
1,000 meters.....1 kilometer

Conversion Table

1 inch......2.54 centimeters
1 foot......0.3048 meter
1 yard......0.9144 meter
1 rod.......5.029 meters
1 furlong...201.17 meters
1 mile......1.6093 kilometers,
            or 1609.3 meters